ELEVATING PREGNANCY

Affirmations and Wisdom
for
Pregnancy & Birth

ANGELA J. BROWN, RN

FOREWORD

"She is a true gift and a blessing... We had the pleasure of having Angela present for the later part of our pregnancy and during the birth of our beautiful son and we could not have done it in a more graceful manner without Angela's inspiration and strengthening affirmations as written in this book. Every pregnant woman needs to read this book to reaffirm within herself that she has the power to move through pregnancy and birth with ease and grace. Having the ability to let go and take each moment as it comes couldn't be more invaluable during this experience and Angela's way of unlocking the potential within is truly her gift."

~John L. Williams, Santa Monica, CA
(1st time Dad)

"This book will be a saving grace for many... If ever there were words that needed to be spoken, written or heard, Angela has written them here in Elevating Pregnancy. She was the doula for both of my home births, and I have seen and heard these words come from her personally and now in the form of this book. Angela has a remarkable gift of expressing her thoughts so eloquently. She has written some of the most important, healing and profound words within this book that will benefit every pregnant woman."

~M. Nguyen-Lopez, San Juan Capistrano, CA
(2nd time Mom)

"**A much needed blessing…** I was deeply blessed to have Angela present during the birth of both of my children. The affirmations in Elevating Pregnancy were the words she uttered during my pregnancies and births. Her energetic presence in my life at those times is manifested in the beautiful words and strength now expressed in this book. Though I do not plan to have any more children, I could not wait to get a copy of Elevating Pregnancy. And it is just as beautiful and moving as I expected it to be. This book will make a lifelong gift not only to any pregnant woman, but any woman who has given birth or who has lost a child along their path to motherhood and wishes to either heal from that experience or move on from it to try again. It will serve as a reminder to those of us who have had the privilege of giving birth, but have struggled since then with our bodies, to look back at what we accomplished, created, and the miraculous things our bodies did to bring our children into being. Angela's words serve to remind all of us of our strength and beauty and power as women and as mothers. The affirmations about things like fear, anxiety, patience, gratitude, and confidence can serve us not only through pregnancy and childbirth, but throughout our entire lives. Elevating Pregnancy will be such an incredible gift to so many women. And to the men out there who have women in your lives… get them this book. Elevating Pregnancy is a divine blessing of Love and Light."

~Smoochiemama, CA
(2nd time Mom)

Copyright © 2020 by DoulaLove'sCreation

Layout and Design: DoulaLove'sCreation & LiveFreeProductions
Author: Angela J. Brown, Founder of DoulaLove'sCreation
Typeset in: InDesign CC

ISBN: 978-1-7346745-0-7

Disclaimer:
The contents of this video/book/article are for informational purposes only and are not a substitute for professional medical advice, diagnosis, or treatment. Always seek the advice of your physician or other qualified health care provider with any questions you have regarding pregnancy or a medical condition, and before undertaking any diet, dietary supplement, exercise, or other health program. Neither Angela J. Brown, RN. nor DoulaLove'sCreation is responsible for any adverse effects resulting from your use of or reliance on any information contained in any video/book/article.

CONTENTS

A Message from the Author

Elevating Pregnancy, Affirmations and Wisdom for Pregnancy & Birth is dedicated to all pregnant women who desire to have a peaceful, calm and empowered birth experience. It was written to support pregnant women in building a consciousness of faith and trust in themselves and in the birth process, throughout their pregnancy and birth experience. Some of you are choosing to experience a VBAC (Vaginal Birth After Cesarean) because you now know that you can birth differently and be more empowered than you were during your previous births. I say, go for it!

Affirmations are positive statements that help one to correct an unsupportive thought and change a negative mindset. Mental awareness and repetition is the key. Practiced regularly, these pregnancy affirmations are a gentle and wonderful way to remind you to keep aligning your thoughts with the energy and activity of love that you are. Fear and love are two different frequencies and cannot occupy the same space at the same time. Where true love is present, fear cannot abide. These affirmations can be read aloud or you can write your own (see end of book). You can speak them into a recorder and listen to them throughout the day or night. You can have the volume turned down low. The great thing is your subconscious mind will still receive the information. Your love frequency and thought vibration will surely rise as you keep affirming anew!

In this day and age, there is so much negativity and fear surrounding childbirth that pregnant women need all the positive support they can get. To align yourself during your child's birth, you must be willing to become aware of the unsupportive thoughts that may occupy your mind during pregnancy, and consciously choose to change them to thoughts that are positive and uplifting. When you do this, you will be "elevating your thoughts" and bringing them into alignment with that which is truth… that your body already knows how to birth, you just have to prepare your mind. May you be willing to invest in yourself and create a daily practice that will support you in developing mental discipline that will create spiritual muscle during your pregnancy and during your birthing time. May your gratitude and love eliminate your fears. May your attention consistently come to a place where you effortlessly behold the beauty and love within yourself, your pregnancy and your child's birth. May you experience the birth of your dreams and enjoy elevating your consciousness in the process.

With love,

Angela

Prayer for Pregnant Mamas

Beloved God, Beloved Father, Beloved Mother, Creator of All Life, Divine Beings of Light, Great Ancestors of Truth, I call upon Your Presence Now…

Thank you for blessing the woman reading this prayer. I bless you from the crown of your head to the soles of your feet. I bless your entire life, your family and the child you have the privilege of carrying within your womb. May the light that you are, be consciously known to you. I proclaim that this light illuminates within your heart, mind and soul, as it illuminates within your child. May you use these affirmations to elevate your thoughts so that you continue to vibrate at a higher frequency during your pregnancy and child's birth. May you turn up the love and trust factor in your life and begin to resonate more with the love that you are and have absolute trust in the birth process. May you grow stronger each day as you read, recite and even write your own affirmations that elevate you in spirit. May you call upon your great ancestral female lineage that have birthed before you and listen to them as they guide you. May you have within your life or call into your life an elder, a woman who can unconditionally support you throughout your pregnancy and birth. May you continue to relinquish the fears and negative perceptions about birth that are blasted in the media and in social interactions. May you attend childbirth education classes that leave you infused with knowledge and feeling empowered about yourself and childbirth. May these classes be life giving and life affirming. May you be daring and allow the warrior woman within you to rise up and proclaim a new thought, a new vision on how to naturally give birth in this day and age. In your surrendered, committed and prayerful use of these affirmations, may you move beyond the "positive words recited" and fully embody and know these words as your own inner truth, know them at a soul level. May you use these nine plus months of pregnancy wisely as you delve inward and do the spiritual work required for you, your child and family. May you build spiritual muscle to sustain you through birth and as a parent. May you build a consciousness of faith and trust in the birth process and in your magnificent self. May you remember at your soul's level that you are loved and that you are loved by the Divine. May you come to know that there is an Innate Intelligence, a Higher Intelligence within you that knows exactly how to give birth, to love and to be a mother. May you experience a sublime birth by the renewing of your mind, body and your spirit.

And so it is. Amen.

Acknowledging the Ancestors

With reverence, love & humility, I acknowledge the female ancestral lineage that have birthed before me. Because of my foremothers, my great-grandmothers I am here today. They birthed naturally and so can I. I call upon their wisdom, power, strength, and confidence, as these qualities are who I am.

Just as my ancestors surround me in this photo, so shall your ancestors surround you during pregnancy, childbirth, and as you parent.

To every woman who is pregnant, To every woman who has birthed a child, To every woman who has birthed and then lost a child, To every woman who has longed to birth her own child but instead became a mother to other children, I acknowledge you and I honor you, the world needs you.

Where would we be without the mothers, grandmothers and great grandmothers of our ancestral female lineage? We need, we require, we must acknowledge the energy and the wisdom of our foremothers who birthed and mothered before us. Their courage and strength runs through our veins… and as women, this is how we know we can birth and birth naturally, if we choose to.

A
Power Greater
than
Myself

I trust that there is a Power greater than me, that lives within me that knows how to birth. I consciously choose to align my thoughts with this Power. I call forth this Inner Power and I am able to give birth in love, grace and ease.

I am one with this Inner Intelligence that lives, moves and breathes as my baby and me.

Acceptance

I give myself permission to accept
myself in my own skin.

I accept myself just as I am.

I am worthy, just as I am.

I am perfect just as I am.

I accept my body just as it is.

I accept my baby just as he/she is.

My acceptance brings me peace.

I accept that my body already knows
how to birth, only my mind can stop
me, if I allow it.

So, I simply choose not to allow it.

Aligning Myself With My Higher Self Now & During My Birthing Time

Right now and during my birthing time, I align my thoughts with my Higher Self and this alignment allows me to keep my attention in the present moment.

Love, breath and gratitude are my only focus.

I consciously use my breath to calm my mind and I use my mind to watch my breath and this keeps me in the present moment.

I joyfully move my body rhythmically into positions that allow me to embrace the powerful birthing sensations I feel. With every breath that I take and every move that I make, I am more confident and empowered. I can do this! I am doing this!

My thoughts and my body are in alignment with the rhythm of my baby. I work with her/him and not against her/him. I consciously send my energy and breath downward to my perineum and exhale completely, as I let go.

I relax my mind, I relax my face, shoulders, hands, thighs, legs, bottom and feet.

I welcome the sensations of my baby's descent through my womb and out of my vagina in joy, with ease and grace.

Birthing in
Alignment

I birth in alignment with the Innate Intelligence that I am.

I am one with this Innate Intelligence.

I surrender to the organic, physiological, scientific, mystical and spiritual Intelligence that...

resides inside of me...

beats my heart, without my help...

breathes my breath, without my help...

births forth my child, with my willingness.

Confidence

I am willing to see the confident nature that lives within me.

It is wonderful to behold my confident self in the mirror each morning.

Each day, as I read and write, recite or listen to my pregnancy and birth affirmations, I feel lighter in my heart and calm in my mind.

In my moments of sitting in meditation, I practice deep breathing and my entire body and mind replenishes itself. I become peaceful in my soul, more confident in myself, and my ability to birth naturally.

I feel confident in myself and it feels wonderful!

Forgiveness

As I take a deep inhale and exhale right now, I place my left hand over my heart and my right hand over my left and close my eyes to center myself in my heart. When I am ready, I open my eyes or keep my eyes closed, and speak words of love and forgiveness to myself.

I forgive myself for judging myself.

I forgive myself for judging myself as not enough.

I forgive myself for judging myself as anger.

I forgive myself for judging myself as fear.

I forgive myself for judging myself as lack and limitation.

I forgive myself for judging myself as weak.

I forgive myself for judging myself as impatience.

I forgive myself for judging myself as shame.

I forgive myself for judging myself as guilt.

I forgive myself for judging myself in comparison to other pregnant women.

I forgive myself for judging myself as doubt and not believing I am able to give birth naturally.

I forgive myself for judging myself as fear that I may not be a good mother.

I forgive myself for judging myself.

Forgiveness opens my heart, renews my mind and soothes my soul.

Gentleness

No matter what I may be experiencing today, I remind myself to be gentle with myself.

I treat myself just as gently as I would my baby learning to latch on to my breast for the first time.

I treat myself as gently as my toddler learning how to take his/her first steps.

I treat myself gently because I am human, because I am a new mother, because I am a seasoned mother, because I am.

I treat myself with gentleness and compassion because it is loving to do so.

I embrace my pregnancy, my birthing and my parenting journey with love, compassion, and gentleness.

Gratitude

My heart is filled with thanksgiving and gratitude.

Thank you God, Divine, Love, Universe for this pregnancy.

Thank you for this child moving within my womb.

Thank you that I am the vessel that houses this beautiful soul.

Thank you Beloved for my Life.

Thank you for this pregnancy and childbirth experience.

Thank you for my patience, strength and perseverance during my birthing time.

Thank you for my health.

Thank you for my child's health.

Thank you for my husband/partners' health.

Thank you for peace, clarity, right thinking and a calm mind.

Thank you Divine for helping me to trust my own intuition.

Thank you for my loving, compassionate and forgiving heart.

Thank you for blessing, supporting and loving every pregnant woman and new mama, papa, and baby upon this earth.

Gratitude
Love
Abundance

I choose to lift my consciousness out of doubt and lack now, and I place my attention on anything that I can be grateful for in this moment.

My gratitude leads to love. My love leads to calm. My calm leads to peace. My peace leads to trust. My trust leads to surrender. My surrender leads to faith. My faith leads to acceptance. My acceptance leads to worthiness. My worthiness leads to my self-love. My self-love leads to my creativity. My creativity leads to my receptivity. My receptivity leads me to the physical manifestation of my abundance.

My love leads to the exchange of energy between myself and another.

My exchange of energy between myself and another leads me to see the light of love of God in all.

I am made new by the renewing of my mind.

I am abundant and this is my truth.

I Am One With My Child

My child within my womb is made from the miraculous love and light of the Creator. I am made from this same light and miraculous love.

I wholeheartedly birth forth my child and myself, as I trust the Innate Intelligence that created us both. I trust myself to birth, and I know that my body knows how to birth forth my child.

During these nine plus months of pregnancy, I do the spiritual work necessary as I vigilantly and joyfully remove any and all mental or emotional blocks that might impede my natural birth intention.

I am one with my child.

Love

This precious child I have the honor and privilege of carrying within my womb is made in the image and likeness of Divine Love.

Therefore, I am created in the image and likeness of this Divine Love, for we are one.

I make a conscious choice and set a clear intention to remember this throughout my pregnancy, during my birthing time and as I parent.

My Hospital Birth Experience

My hospital birth experience is how I believe it to be for me.

My mind and heart are open to love and experiencing the most loving and supportive birth during my hospital stay. Throughout my birthing time and my postpartum recovery, I am receiving excellent care from each hospital professional that my husband/partner and I interact with.

My hospital birth experience is filled with love, support, encouragement and respect for my choices. I trust and know that my baby and I are safe.

I am fully informed of my choices and about any medical procedures that may be recommended to me. I am knowledgeable and empowered.

Every doctor, midwife, nurse, and hospital staff person supports me from a consciousness of love, patience and compassion. They speak to me with the voice of love and touch me with the hand of love.

Each person that enters my room, during my hospital stay, does so with love, joy and peace in their heart. Their energy magnifies the radiant love, peace and joy that illuminates from my heart and my family's heart.

I feel and have felt so incredibly, nurtured and cared for throughout my hospital experience. I am deeply grateful to all the hospital staff that attended to my baby, my husband/partner and myself.

Thank you everyone for loving and holding sacred space for us through the most extraordinary and miraculous time of our lives. We appreciate you all.

My Pregnant Body

I am beautiful. My belly is beautiful. My body is swelling in love for my child that is growing within my womb. My child is healthy and so am I.

I love and embrace being pregnant. I love the new sensations I experience within my changing body.

Even though I may be experiencing nausea or vomiting, I trust and know that my body regulates itself and that my hormones, my baby, and myself are in divine harmonious and healthy alignment.

I love witnessing firsthand, everyday the miraculous growth of my child within me.

I choose to behold my child's birth from a consciousness of love, peace and grace.

I remind myself that the physical sensations of birth are temporary, and I use my long deep breathing to move me through any discomfort.

This pregnancy is a journey of love, self-acceptance, surrender and growth. I flow easily and effortlessly with my changing body.

My heart is full of love and gratitude for my baby, my husband/partner and myself. I realize that gratitude is the quickest way for me to return to my loving.

On Anger or Resentment

I honor my emotional body and what is present for me in the moment. I may be feeling anger or resentful right now and I know this feeling will not last, nor do I want it to, so I am making a new choice now.

I choose love now. I choose forgiveness now. I choose to forgive myself for judging my own anger. I choose to forgive the person or situation I perceive has caused my anger.

I, and I alone am responsible for my reaction to any given person or situation.

I am allowed to feel my feelings and honor what is present; however, I do not choose to set up residence at "Camp Anger Lodge".

I acknowledge that my anger or upset is showing me something about myself and I am willing to look at it, be honest and let it go.

Through these fleeting emotions, I remember to bring my attention back to my breath, back to my loving.

Self-love and self-forgiveness are my intention through this pregnancy and beyond, not anger and upset.

I let go now and I allow love to reign supreme within me and all around me.

On Anxiety

Right now, I STOP

I take a deep inhale, and a long exhale

I take another deep inhale and long exhale

and another one

and another one

and another one…

I am more than this anxiety and panic.

My breath brings me back to my heart center and I am grateful I can continue on from this moment.

One moment at a time and one breath at a time. I allow calmness. I allow peace. I am free. All is well.

On Communicating
with Baby When
Feeling Ungrounded

When I am experiencing emotional ups and downs, feelings of fear, sadness, tears of anger, frustration, irritability toward myself, my partner or someone else, I acknowledge these feelings and I know that they shall pass.

I remember, it is most important to communicate with my baby and I let him/her know that I love them.

What mommy is experiencing are my feelings and these feelings and emotions are mine, not yours. You, my little one, are safe and secure inside of me. I'm okay, baby, I am working through all of these human emotions so that I can birth you in grace.

Beloved child, my emotional triggers or upsets are mine and have nothing to do with your innocence and the love that you are.

You, my sweet baby, are spiritually, emotionally and physically whole, thriving and living in pure joy! For you are a Child of God of the Most High and so am I.

Just know my love, all is well, you are safe, mama's got you and I love you.

On Feeling
Overwhelmed

When I am feeling overwhelmed, I remember to let go of the idea that things need to be perfect and done in a certain way and at a certain time.

I make the choice in this moment to stop and take some deep breaths.

It is okay for me to give myself five minutes of stillness to deeply breathe and gain clarity.

From this point of stillness and breath, I choose the most important task or tasks that must be completed today.

I remember that feelings of overwhelm can create stagnation and more feelings of overwhelm.

So right now, in this moment, I am making a new choice for myself.

I take the time now, to acknowledge and appreciate myself right where I am.

I appreciate you, _____
(write your name here & speak it aloud)

I appreciate you, _____
(Look in the mirror)

I appreciate you, _____
(Say this aloud)

Right now, I am choosing to be accepting and gentle with myself.

I am doing the best I can and this is enough.

I reprioritize my lists and I set reasonable goals for myself.

I embrace this state of calm and peace I have created within myself, for myself and for my baby.

On Induction

If the suggestion or need for induction shows up in my pregnancy and birthing experience, I choose to remain calm, to listen and to learn what my options are.

Throughout my pregnancy and during my last trimester, I choose to be physically proactive by exercising and eating healthy. I willingly and gratefully practice natural induction techniques, walking, curb walking, loving making, dancing, acupuncture, chiropractic care, nipple stimulation or whatever is healthy and intuitively feels right for my body and spirit.

If induction becomes necessary for me, it is my responsibility to truly understand why induction is being suggested.

If induction is necessary, I give myself permission to receive the induction method(s) suggested by communicating to my body and my baby about what will be happening. I understand that just because I may be induced, it is still possible for me to have a natural vaginal birth without further medication.

I let go now. I trust my body to receive the induction and I trust that my body knows how to respond and does so quickly, effectively and harmoniously.

I am safe. My baby is safe. My baby is healthy and continues to thrive within my womb and I communicate this to him/her. I'll see you soon baby. I love you.

On Meditation

Meditation is a vital part of learning how to live well and to birth well. Learning to breathe deeply is a constant theme throughout this book.

We live in a time of a variety of childbirth education classes and books written on birth and parenting; however, our female ancestral lineage knew about the breath and its importance throughout life and especially during childbirth.

If the breath is shallow, the body will be tense during birth. If the body is tense and rigid during birth, a woman will feel more intensity and pain. In other words, she will move her energy upward (clinching) when her baby wants to move down and out. This is known as resistance, resisting what is. Birth requires flow and fluidity.

The flow of childbirth is to send the energy downward. In order to send the energy downward, one must learn to breathe well and send the exhaled breath down and out through the perineum.

Meditation is learning how to gently still the mind with long deep breathing to help a pregnant woman throughout pregnancy and birth.

You can begin with a one-minute meditation, increase to three minutes, and increase to five minutes and eventually to more time, which is recommended. You can also play soft meditative music, focus on a mantra or speak it softly aloud.

All you have to do is...

Use your mind to watch your breath and use your breath to calm your mind, then repeat.

Every time your mind wanders off to another thought, when you catch the mind wandering, bring it back to watching the breath, then repeat.

Release any judgments that you are not doing it correctly and be gentle with yourself.

Meditation helps you to develop and trust your intuition and you will need this intuition as you birth and as you parent.

Enjoy your daily meditations and the peace it brings to you and your baby.

One Birthing Wave
at a Time

I remind myself to focus on one birthing wave at a time.

I will not waste my mental time thinking about a birthing wave that is gone or one that is coming.

One birthing wave at a time.

When I experience a birthing wave, I allow my deep breathing, my physical rhythmic movements and my focused and calm mind to move me through it.

When it is over, I completely let it go and I rest.

I use my mind to watch my breath, and I use my breath to calm my mind.

I am safe. I am love. I am loved.

I got this!

Opening to Financial Wealth and Wellbeing for Our Growing Family

I open my heart to receive the gifts of the Spirit that indwell me.

I realize that financial worry does not serve me.

Right here, in this moment, I breathe. I take one breath at a time.

I am abundant.

No matter what it looks like, I continue to proclaim.

I am abundant.

I let go of the fear and the false perceptions that I am not worthy and that I am not enough.

I am abundant.

I am willing to grow beyond what I physically see or what I "see" in my bank account.

I am abundant.

All that I desire has already been given to me.

The Universe is abundant and so am I.

I am enough. I am worthy. All of my needs are met.

I/We can more than afford this child and the timing of this pregnancy is perfect.

I am worthy because I breathe. I am worthy because I am alive.

I am worthy because I was born this way. And I am a child of the Most High God.

I am worthy because this Magnificent, Abundant Universe indwells me.

Patience

Throughout my pregnancy, especially as the end of my pregnancy approaches, I choose to remain patient, calm and centered within my heart. I do not allow others' impatience, excited phone calls or text messages to affect the calm peace of my mind.

I breathe deeply and I make choices that support me in remaining calm. I can choose to turn off the phone, put it on silent or leave an outgoing message thanking everyone for their well wishes.

I believe in my child and I know that she or he knows exactly the right time to be born.

I trust my baby. I trust my body. I trust myself.

Proclaiming
Health and
Wholeness
When Feeling Out
of Alignment

When I am feeling unwell or out of alignment, I breathe deeply and allow myself to just be, without judging myself.

I take deep slow breaths in, filling up my belly and lungs with this incredible breath that is my Life Force and I slowly exhale and relax.

With each conscious deep breath, the tension, mental anxiety, and the physical discomfort releases from my body and my mind and I am calm and peace-filled.

As I place my attention on each inhale and exhale, I am feeding every cell, atom, and organ of my body temple with renewed energy, health, wholeness, vitality and aliveness!

And, I proclaim that...

"Every cell, atom, organ of my body is infused with the healing light of God.

Every cell, atom, organ of my body is infused with the healing light of God.

Every cell, atom, organ of my body is infused with the healing light of God.

Every cell, atom, organ of my body is infused with the healing light of Love.

Every cell, atom, organ of my body is infused with the healing light of Love.

Every cell, atom, organ of my body is infused with the healing light of Love.

Every cell, atom, organ of my body is infused with the healing light of Peace.

Every cell, atom, organ of my body is infused with the healing light of Peace.

Every cell, atom, organ of my body is infused with the healing light of Peace."

Rising Above Others' Unsupportive Birth Stories

When I hear another woman speak about her birth story in an unsupportive way, when she talks about her perception of the birth she experienced or one that a friend or relative experienced, I take a slow deep breath and I consciously visualize myself infused with and surrounded in healing white light.

With each inhale and exhale, the Light of Divine Love fills my being and I know my baby and I are safe.

I acknowledge that this is this woman's experience and perception about birth, and it has nothing to do with me or my birth vision and intention.

I am always protected and directed as my mental and emotional bodies are replenished with my own visions of a peaceful birth. I place my attention on my birth intention and speak my pregnancy and birth affirmations.

I affirm and accept right now that every cell, atom, organ of my body is infused with the healing light of love.

I allow this woman or any woman the dignity of her own birth story, and I know that I do not have to make her story or her birth experience my own and this is such a relief.

I breathe deeply and I hold true to my birth intention for my child's sacred and safe birth experience.

On The Sensations
of Childbirth

The sensations of childbirth require a breath that is long and deep, a mind that can touch the stillness of its own soul, a heart that is open and surrendered and a body that is relaxed and fluid.

A mind that touches the stillness is a mind that watches the breath and lets go of the mental chatter that is not in alignment with the natural order and fluidity of birth.

Resistance happens in the mind first then travels to the body, if you are not aware of this or unaware of the thoughts you are thinking, how can you change the thought or behavior, and relax?

If your mind says, "I can't do this, I can't take it." Your body's response is, "No, you can't."

When your mind says, "I can do this." Your body's automatic response is, "Yes, you can."

Choose to breathe deeply with each birthing wave you experience and remember that your deep breathing is your letting go and allowing your body to do its most perfect work, which is to birth forth your beautiful baby.

The Little Girl

If the little girl in me rears her head during my birthing time, I remind myself that being out of control or choosing hysteria is not what is needed here. A little girl does not know how to give birth, but a woman does!

I am such a WOMAN.

I am fully anchored within my feminine power.

In my mind, I look my little-self square in the eyes and I clearly let her know that I've got this! I give her a hug and kiss, I reassure her that she is perfectly safe, and I put her to bed for a long, deep and healing sleep.

I use my conscious mind and deep breaths to refocus and I get back on track to my empowered birth. My heart is open, I am re-centered in my loving power and I am allowing each and every birthing wave to bring me closer to holding my baby in my arms.

I surrender to my body as I align my thoughts to the truth that my body already knows how to give birth, and I allow it to birth.

Trust and Faith

I trust the natural progression and innate intelligence of pregnancy and childbirth.

I trust my body and I know that it possesses everything it needs to sustain this pregnancy, nourish my child and birth forth my child, with my willingness.

I trust myself and give thanks that I am able to carry my child full-term.

My heart is open, I am surrendered, I trust my birthing process and I know it is just right for my baby and me.

Everyday I grow in confidence in my abilities to experience natural childbirth.

I love myself. I trust myself.
I have faith in myself.

I confidently birth forth my child in Love, Joy & Gratitude.

I love my baby. I trust my baby.
I have faith in my baby.

I trust that my baby knows exactly what to do to move through and out of me.

I have faith in myself and I know exactly how to care for my child when he/she is born.

VBAC

I am experiencing a natural, non-medicated, vaginal birth. With joy and grace, I fully embrace my VBAC experience.

I am now wiser and more confident about pregnancy and childbirth than before. My heart is receptive to my birthing process and I am willing and ready for it.

During my pregnancy, I prepare my mind and my body so that I am fully open and available to experiencing my beautiful, healthy VBAC.

I surrender to my body's Inner Intelligence and I trust and accept the natural progression of my child descending through my womb and out of my vagina.

My child, this pregnancy and birthing time is all about love and gratitude, and this is where I joyously keep my attention right now, and as I birth.

Warrior Woman

I am a Warrior Woman

A Warrior Woman knows the purpose of pregnancy and birth and she does not waste her time during pregnancy worrying.

A Warrior Woman is fearless. I am fearless.

I am a Warrior Woman because I breathe.

I am a Warrior Woman because my heart beats.

I am a Warrior Woman because I am growing a sacred life within me.

I am a Warrior Woman because I am a spiritual being and mother.

A Warrior Woman rises through indecision and confusion. She goes within and listens to her Higher Self, Her Divine Self so that she gains clarity in order to know what to do and when to do it.

A Warrior Woman fills her inner cup by doing the spiritual work during pregnancy. She communicates within herself, she communicates with her partner and listens to her baby and knows just what her body and baby needs.

She prays, she meditates, she journals, she walks, she listens to her deepest wisdom in the silence of her own heart.

I now activate my inner Warrior Woman by calling her forth. Warrior Woman that I am, come forth now and show me this version of myself that I have yet to meet. I know that you exist within me, and I acknowledge your presence now.

Create Your Own
Affirmations

_____

_____

_____

_____

_____

_____

_____

_____

_____

_____

_____

_____

_____

_____

_____

_____

Made in the USA
Monee, IL
04 April 2023